Silver Mittens

PALMETTO
P U B L I S H I N G
Charleston, SC
www.PalmettoPublishing.com

Silver Mittens
Copyright © 2023 by John.J.Mullen

Hardcover ISBN: 979-8-8229-2242-6
Paperback ISBN: 979-8-8229-2243-3
eBook ISBN: 979-8-8229-2244-0

Silver Mittens

John . J . Mullen

Chapter 1

It was a hot and humid July day in the working-class town of Lowell, Massachusetts, just thirty minutes north of Boston. In a section of Lowell called Belvedere stood a two-story house. It was a two-family home, but only one family lived in it. There was a peculiar round stained-glass window at the top of the stairs in the second-floor hallway.

Inside the house lived two adults and four kids. The two adults were Raymond Mullen Sr., a machinist at Raytheon. He worked in the Experimental Division, building parts for bombs and missiles and parts for the space shuttle as well. The other was his wife, Charolitte, who worked in the cafeteria at Wang Laboratories and did wine and cheese parties for the Wang executives. She also made cakes on the side.

The four kids consisted of two girls and two boys. Kelly, who left the house when she was only fifteen years old, was the oldest. Of the two boys, Ray was nine years old. Kathy was the second-oldest child at thirteen. Johnny was the youngest at eight years old. Johnny was born on June 1, and Ray was born on June 2 a year earlier—Irish twins, some would say.

Ray was nine when his sister Kelly moved out, and Johnny was eight. Kelly moved in with her boyfriend, who at the time was ten years older than she was. Two weeks after Kelly left the house, a life-changing event happened.

It was one of those hazy summer Sunday afternoons. Ray heard a loud bang, shouting, and screaming while he was in his bedroom. He ran from his bedroom to see what the noise and screaming were all about. He bolted from his bedroom to the living room, where his dad was accusing his mom of sleeping with his uncle John, one of Ray's favorite uncles.

The younger son, Johnny, heard screaming and yelling as well. Johnny was outside playing wiffleball in the backyard. He was at home plate, up at bat. It wasn't a real home plate; they used the blueberry bush as home plate. As soon as he heard his mother's screams and cries for help, he dropped the bat, ran inside the house, and flew upstairs, where the screams were coming from.

Just as Johnny reached the top of the stairs, he saw his father on top of his mother, about to punch her again. He had already struck her in the face several times. An instant before he tried to strike her again, Johnny saw Ray dive at his father and knock him off his mother.

Raymond Sr. looked at Ray and smiled with an evil grin. Then he got up from the floor and staggered to the couch with a drunken walk. As he had been drinking all morning and into the early afternoon, he passed out minutes later.

The next-door neighbor, Joe, called the police after he heard the screams from his kitchen. The police arrived fifteen minutes later. Ray Sr. was still passed out on the couch when they knocked on the door. There were two policemen who responded to the call.

Once the police officers entered the dwelling, they questioned the mother. After questioning the mother, the police officers walked over to the father, still passed out on the couch.

One of the policemen tapped him on his back with his nightstick. There was no response. He did not respond to the policeman tapping him on his back, so the police officer's partner grabbed Ray and shook him. There was still no response. The officers then started slapping him in the face to get him to come around. Ray Sr. came out of it and started throwing punches at the officers. One of the officers dove on him and grabbed both of his hands and yanked them behind his back. Then the officer proceeded to handcuff him.

The officers stood him up on his feet and walked him down the stairs and out of the house. As the officers were putting him in the police car, the younger son, Johnny, watched from upstairs, looking through the peculiar circular stained-glass window.

Johnny had a very sad look on his face, and he had a feeling of no hope for an end to this situation the family was stuck in.

Kelly, who had already moved away, came to visit. She came over after she received the call that her dad had been arrested for domestic violence.

Her dad passed out again once he was booked and put in his jail cell. The father came to from his morning and afternoon of drinking to find himself in the drunk tank, also known as a jail cell. With a pounding headache and as angry as could be, he started screaming at the top of his lungs for his one phone call. "I am allowed a phone call. It's my right to have one phone call," he kept yelling.

Charolitte took the kids to her mother's house.

Ray was released from jail after posting bond. He had to wait two hours till the bail bondsman got there. He was charged with domestic violence and assault and battery on a police officer. He was also charged with criminal threatening.

Once the bail bondsman arrived, Ray paid him and signed his paperwork. He was released on his own recognizance.

When he got home to an empty house, he went to a hotel after grabbing some clothes. He made arrangements several weeks later to pick up the rest of his things. There was a police officer there to make sure nothing became violent. Ray Sr. picked up his things and left the house without any incident.

Chapter 2

The embattled couple had been together for fifteen years. Charolitte took the three kids and moved to a section of Lowell called the Highlands. The move lasted late into the night. They moved with the help of Charolitte's dad. Kelly could not help with the move because she had gotten the news she was pregnant.

Ray Sr. got an apartment just on the other side of the fence from the kids' new apartment in Princeton Village in the Highlands.

After their parents' divorce was final, the boys saw their dad on the weekends until there was an incident with the police and their dad at his new apartment.

The boys' dad held an ax to their throats and called their mom and threatened to kill them. The police showed up, busted down the door, tackled their dad and cuffed him, dragged him out of the apartment, and put him in the paddy wagon.

Just a week earlier, Johnny's dad was driving him down the street, and just before they were about to hit a tree head-on, the dad looked at Johnny and said, "I will kill us both." At the last possible moment, the dad yanked the steering wheel to pull away from the tree. The car spun out and did circles, almost flipping over, but it didn't.

Johnny never told anyone about the incident in the car, but he still has nightmares to this very day as an adult. Ray Sr. abused the two boys physically, emotionally, and sexually. The boys never told anyone of the abuse.

They were able to afford the new apartment with a program called Section Eight—money kicked in by the state to help people who can't afford an apartment otherwise. Within months of being in the new apartment in Princeton Village, the mother was dating a carpenter named Skippy. But Johnny knew it wouldn't last because Skippy was such a nice guy.

Skippy knew Charolitte's boys liked playing checkers, so he made them a coffee table that had a checkerboard carved into it. Charolitte could not handle being treated nice because of her own emotional issues of self-loathing and poor self-image. It turned out that Johnny was dead-on accurate about his earlier prediction of Charolitte and Skippy not working out. In her mind it was over, but she did not tell Skippy and continued to have sex with him.

Charolitte called an appliance repairman to fix her oven. Johnny's aunt Paula encouraged her sister to call him for a date because she had been eyeing and flirting with him the whole service call. The repairman's name was George. She was flirting with him heavily and could not stop talking about him after he left. Charolitte had seen the repairman's name on his uniform, so she called the appliance store, Dick's TV, based out of Lawrence, Massachusetts.

The secretary answered the phone and said, "Dick's TV. How can I help you?"

Charolitte responded, "You had a repairman come to my apartment and repair my oven. My address is 144 Black Brook Drive in Lowell, Massachusetts. May I speak with him?"

The secretary summoned George. He picked up the phone and said, "Hello. George speaking."

Charolitte paused and said, "This is Charolitte. Do you remember me?"

George replied, "Yes, I remember you. I wanted to flirt back with you, but I didn't want to get in trouble with my work for doing so."

She asked him if he would like to go on a date. George said yes and agreed to get together with her on Saturday night. They decided on seven o'clock at the Olympia Restaurant.

Later, Charolitte called George and told him she was running behind schedule. But the real reason was that Skippy the carpenter was not out of the picture yet and not out of the apartment yet that night. She told Skippy she had plans with her girlfriends and could not hang out with him the rest of the night.

George showed up for their date in the Dick's TV work van. His nationality was Greek, and he wanted to impress her, so he took her to a place where he would be knowledgeable about the food and customs. So he picked the Olympia. It was a Greek restaurant.

Charolitte arrived at the restaurant at seven thirty. George was already inside, in the waiting-to-be-seated area. They exchanged pleasantries once Charolitte came in.

"Hi. How are you, George?"

"Hi. I'm good. Great to see you again," replied George.

"Sorry I'm late," Charolitte said. "Have you been here long?"

"No, not at all," he replied.

"Your table is ready," said the hostess, whose name was Tiffany. "Follow me to your table. Your waitress, Natalie, will be with you in a moment."

Natalie came to the table minutes later and asked, "Can I start you off with a drink?"

Charolitte replied, "I'll have a mudslide."

George said, "I'll have a Coke."

Charolitte asked, "George, why no alcohol?"

He replied, "I'm a recovering alcoholic."

The waitress returned with their drinks and said, "Are you ready to order some food?"

"We need a minute or so," said George.

The waitress left and went to attend to her other customers.

While she was gone, the two started to talk and get to know each other. George said to Charolitte, "Did you know I'm Greek?" He also claimed his natural father had mob ties. George said he was pissed that his mom had kept him away from that. He thought he could have worked for the mob and become rich. George was originally from Jamaica Plains in Boston, Massachusetts.

Charolitte was a conformist and would do anything she could to keep a man happy so she could be taken care of financially.

While Charolitte was on her date with George, Skippy was helping a friend fix his kitchen cabinets and did not know Charolitte was on a date. Skippy was still coming over on weekends, and everything was going well in his relationship with Charolitte as far as he knew.

The waitress came back to the table and asked, "Have you decided on some food?"

Charolitte replied, "Yes, I'll have the lamb and rice."

George said, "That sounds good. I'll have the same."

"Will that be all?" the waitress said.

"Yes, thank you," replied Charolitte.

The waitress came back to the table twenty minutes later with the lamb-and-rice plates. Natalie said, "Enjoy your meal."

The couple finished their meals, and George brought Charolitte back to her apartment.

They got out of George's company van. George walked her to her door, and then Charolitte said to him, "Would you like to come in for a nightcap?"

He replied, "Yes, I would."

They entered her apartment. Charolitte got George a Coke. They sat in the kitchen and talked while George drank his Coke. Once he finished, he got up from the table and went over to Charolitte and started kissing her. After several minutes of kissing and heavy petting, they stopped, and Charolitte said, "It's getting late. I need to get to sleep. I have to work tomorrow."

"Okay," George said. "I really enjoyed our date. Good night, Charolitte."

After dating for only a short amount of time, Charolitte invited him to move in. He happily accepted her offer.

Skippy was playing checkers with Johnny when George walked through the apartment door with an overnight bag with his clothes. Ray was on the couch watching TV. Skippy said to Charolitte, "Who the fuck is this?"

Charolitte said, "I'm sorry; things are not working out for us. This is George, and we've been on a few dates. He is going to be moving in with me."

Skippy took the few things he had at the apartment for when he stayed over. On his way out the door, he said, "I hope you enjoy your coffee table!" The one he had hand carved a checkerboard into for her sons.

The two boys were sad to see Skippy go. They really liked him and felt bad that he was leaving so hurt and angry. "The body is not even cold yet," the youngest said to George.

"Wow. Would you jump in my grave that?" remarked Ray.

The new boyfriend was not only a recovering alcoholic, but he also had a gambling problem and an issue with violence that would surface later on.

Chapter 3

Charolitte and George moved the boys and Kathy to a section of Lowell called Pawtucketville. The happened only a few months after George had moved into the apartment on Black Brook drive in the Highlands.

The new apartment in Pawtucketville was in a quiet neighborhood with a church on the end of their new street. Their new address was 84 Fifth Avenue.

Two streets up there was a variety store that sold homemade beans on Saturday, and they had

Marcus Childhood Friend

miniature loaves of bread to soak up the juice from the beans. It was called Martin's Variety. They also sold Big League Chew and Swedish fish there. Johnny's friend Scott lived upstairs. His dad ran a stereo shop from the back of the convenience store.

On the corner of Martins Variety was Johnny's, Ray's, and Scott's bus stop for school.

At this time, Ray was training at Ramalho's West End Boxing Gym, located in downtown Lowell by Elliott's Hot Dogs. He was training alongside Joey Ramalho, and they were being trained by Mr. Ramalho, a.k.a. Arthur Ramalho. Mr. Ramalho ran the gym and trained young fighters. Mr. Ramalho also worked a full-time job along with running the gym.

When Charolitte moved the boys again, Ray moved over to a gym in a section of Lowell called the Acre. The gym was called Acre Boxing. It was there that he finished his training for the amateur boxing tournament called the Silver Mittens.

The owner was Ray Machmannis, a.k.a. Ouchy. It was a very small gym, but it was big enough to have a boxing ring in it.

There were trainers, Dennis Rudy and Dicky Ecklund, for Micky Ward. Ouchy did some training as well. Ray, Richie Collins, and Micky Ward all trained there until Ouchy passed away. Rudy trained Ray and prepared him for the Silver Mittens.

Ray before his first fight in the Silver Mittens tournament

The Silver Mittens boxing tournament was held at the Lowell Boys Club. Ray was dedicated to his training for the Silver Mittens, and Rudy was working hard to have him ready for it.

Ray won all his fights, making it to the final match. His opponent in the final match was a fighter he had faced earlier in the year. Ray, also known as M&M, which stood for Motor Mouth, had knocked his opponent out the first time they fought.

The bell rang for M&M's final bout in the tournament. He went after his opponent right away. But his opponent just kept running from him, trying to frustrate him. His opponent's strategy of trying to frustrate him did not work. M&M kept his cool and kept scoring on his opponent the whole boxing match.

Ouchy Rudy Ray's Trainers

The bell rang to end the match. They both returned to their corners to await the judges' decision. Then both fighters went to the center of the ring with their trainers and wait for the referee to raise their hand in victory. The announcement was made: "Ray Mullen from Acre Boxing wins!" Ray was there with his trainer, Dennis Rudy, and Ouchy.

The referee raised his hands in victory. Both M&M and Rudy were elated with their win.

The tournament continued until all the weight classes had fought. Then they announced the outstanding fighter. The announcement came over the PA system. "And outstanding fighter goes to Acre Boxing's Ray Mullen!"

M&M and Dennis Rudy celebrated. They had the trophy ceremony, and M&M picked up his trophy for winning his division and for winning outstanding fighter. Then they

Interview after fight

Ray's final bout in silver mittens tournament

interviewed M&M. After talking with the interviewers, Ray talked with and posed for pictures with friends and family. Then he headed home with Johnny.

Once Ouchy passed away, all the fighters moved from Acre Boxing back to Ramalho's West End Gym at its new location on Ghorm Street. After you crossed a small bridge, the gym door was up the stairs on the right. There was a sign on the door in the winter months saying "Make sure your dues are paid up in the winter to pay for the heat."

All of Ray's boxing trainers commented that he had fast hands, fast feet, and a hard right hand. Ray also liked to talk fast and taunt the people he fought. That was how he got the nickname M&M.

During their time in Pawtucketville, the two boys stayed away from their apartment as much as possible to avoid the turbulent mess that always went on in it. And for that matter, any one of the apartments they lived in.

One time, inside the house, their sister Kathy threw a butcher knife at Ray from across the kitchen table. Ray was so pissed that he punched Kathy right in her nose. Ray was fifteen at the time. He spent most of his time at the boxing gym. But when he was not at the gym, he spent time with his then girlfriend Lucia.

Johnny was on the McAvinnue Junior High wrestling team and the basketball team, and he started a school newspaper with his friend Thomas Andreoli. He also played on the Pawtucketville youth organization baseball team with

Lawrence and Marty Elliott and Scott O'Malley. He played for the Twins when he was in seventh and eighth grades. The Twins won the championship. Johnny fondly remembers the dances and friends he met there at McAve Junior High.

When Johnny was not playing sports for the junior high or for the Twins baseball team, he spent a lot of his time across the street with his friend Dave and his dad, Mr. St. Armond. Johnny also spent time hanging out at his good friend Sully's (Sean Sullivan) house. At Mr. St. Armond's house, Johnny and Dave would play football, wiffleball, and basketball, and they would also go swimming.

The neighborhood girls Kim Ericson and Dawn Ayotte would come over and watch them play sometimes. They would also play reliveo with Marcus Reyes, Dawn, Kim, Dave, Ray, Shane, and Sean Sullivan. For reliveo, you would have two teams. One team counted off, and the other team went to hide. After you finished counting, usually to fifty, you would go find the team that went to hide. You would catch a person from the team you were competing against and say, "One, two, three, you're caught." And then you would take them to your home base, which was your jail.

You usually had one team member guard the jail because if you didn't, one of the opposing team members could come by, tag their teammate in jail, and say, "One, two, three, reliveo," and then their teammate could break out of jail and run free.

Johnny, Ray, Dawn, Kim, and sometimes Cheryle would play spin the bottle. They would all sit in a circle with a bottle in the middle. When it was your turn, you spun the bottle, and whomever the narrow end of the bottle was pointing to when it stopped spinning, you had to kiss them.

The girls of the neighborhood would sometimes join them when they went swimming. Ray ate at Marcus's house all the time. He loved his mom's cooking, especially the Spanish rice. His mom told Ray "you can eat here anytime". "But when I give you food to go in Tupperware you have to bring it back, or you can't eat here anymore". Ray always brought the leftovers to his brother. Ray's mom caught him with the food and took the Tupperware, and said she was not going to give it back. Ray went up the hill to Marcus's house crying, and told his mom he could not get the Tupperware from his mom. Marcus's mom was so angry she went down the hill to Ray's house with her husband. She banged on the door loudly, and was screaming for Charolitte to come out. She finally came to the door and she said "you should not be feeding my son". Marcus's mom yelled back "you should be feeding him then". Marcus's dad kept saying to his wife "don't hit her". After the two ladies were done yelling back and forth at each other she finally gave Marcus's mother back her Tupperware, and she went back up the hill to her house but she was still really angry.

Ray and Johnny would pull fun pranks on each other. They would open up their bedroom door just enough so that a sneaker could rest on the top of the door and wait in the bedroom till the other entered, and the sneaker would fall on the other's head.

Things were okay for the first few months in Pawtucketville. Then George—they had married after moving to Pawtucketville—started beating the two boys regularly and being verbally abusive to them. He also on multiple occasions threatened to take Johnny's clothes off and fuck him!

Kathy started dating a new guy, Brian. Brian hit Kathy in the face, and news of this got back to George and Ray. George confronted Brian on the street. Punches flew, and a fight ensued. Fifteen minutes later Ray got there and joined in on the fight.

Ray started punching Brian in the ribs. Brian, who was much older and stronger than Ray at the time, punched Ray in the face. The punch stunned Ray for a minute, and he sat down. But then he got back up and continued to punch Brian—in the ribs this time, much harder and with more force.

The cops came and broke up the fight. No charges were filed. Kathy did not leave him, even after he hit her again on several other occasions. This went on for years. They would fight, breakup, and then get back together.

Johnny was training as a Greco-Roman wrestler at the same time. He started wrestling in the sixth grade at the Lowell Boys Club. In the seventh grade, Johnny took third place in the city wrestling tournament. He made it to the eighth-grade city tournament wrestling finals. The final match for the championship was held at Lowell High School.

One of the judges screamed out, "Stop fucking around and pin him, Johnny!" So Johnny pinned him to win the city wrestling tournament in his weight class, and the crowd roared. Sully, one of the point judges and the oldest of the Sullivan boys, was the one who screamed out, "Stop fucking around and pin him."

The crowd roared when Johnny won because his opponent had walked onto the wrestling mat all cocky and swung his arms way out to the side and puffed his chest out. Ray yelled out, "You did it, brother."

The following year Johnny continued to wrestle and was on the Greater Lowell Regional Tech High School wrestling team. Ray continued to box, and he was also on the high school swim team. Just before George moved the boys to Lawrence in the middle of Johnny's sophomore year, Ray Sr. took Johnny and Ray to Johnny's senior league baseball field, Flagg's, to throw the football around. However, it was more about Ray Sr. wanting to see if he could still throw the football farther than his sons.

He threw the ball a little further than Ray and Johnny. Ray Sr. said, "What are you? A bunch of fags? You can't throw it further than me. I'm old and all fagged out." What Ray Sr. didn't know was that the boys let him win so that he wouldn't flip out like he often did. When he didn't throw it far enough, he whipped the ball at Johnny's head, but Johnny ducked just in time. Ray Sr. would often fly off the handle for no reason at all.

Chapter 4

That was the last time Ray Sr. saw the boys before George moved them to Lawrence with Charolitte and Kathy. George said it would be easier for him and his work commute if they all moved to Lawrence, where his job at Dick's TV was located. So Charolitte uprooted the boys once again and moved them to Lawrence.

Ray was not happy. He did not want to move to Lawrence. The whole life that he had built was in Lowell. He asked to stay with one of his uncles, but his mother didn't let him.

Charolitte and George packed up and moved the three kids to a section of Lawrence called Tower Hill. Johnny missed out on getting his varsity letterman's jacket for wrestling that he was going to receive at the end of the wrestling season for his sophomore year. Ray could not continue his boxing because it was too long a ride, and he had to work in the appliance store after he got out of school.

Shortly after George Healy, Charolitte, and the kids moved to Lawrence, George was offered an opportunity to take over the appliance store. The owner of Dick's TV groomed him and set him up pretty well to be on his own. He talked Ray into coming to work for him and also convinced him to quit school because he was short staffed and needed another appliance repairman. George didn't want to pay the salary of a repairman who was already fully trained, so he persuaded Ray to quit school and come to work for him so he could save money. Ray was a very quick study and really smart, so he picked it up fast. Johnny also worked in the appliance store but did so after school and on Saturdays. He did appliance delivery. George bought old appliances, fixed them up, and sold them.

Just a few months after they moved into their apartment on Yale Street in Tower Hill, there was an episode of violence. George and Ray were in the kitchen, and an argument started. Then George started punching Ray, first in the face and then in the ribs. George continued to punch Ray in the ribs while Charolitte just stood there watching and saying nothing.

Kelly was there visiting and saw the whole thing unfold. She said to her mother, "Aren't you going to do anything? He's beating your child."

Charolitte just walked away from Kelly and went into her bedroom and shut the door. George continued to beat Ray, so Kelly called the police.

The police arrived twenty minutes later and knocked on the door forcefully. One of the officers shouted with a stern voice, "Lawrence Police Department. Open up."

Kelly came to the door and let the officers in.

"What happed here?" said one of the officers. "Is there a legal guardian here? Can I speak to the mother?"

Charolitte came out of the bedroom to speak to the officers. She didn't give them much information, so the officers asked Kelly, "Do you know what happened here, miss?"

"Yes. He beat my brother Ray, who is just a teenager. This man here"—she pointed to George—"is the asshole that beat my brother."

"Where is Ray now?" asked the officer.

"He's in his bedroom," Kelly said.

"Which way is his bedroom? Show me. We want to speak with him."

Ray's bedroom door was closed. The officers knocked, and one of them said, "It's the Lawrence police. May we come in? We need to talk to you."

Ray said "Come in" in a low muffled voice.

The officers entered Ray's bedroom to find him lying on his bed in massive amounts of pain, groaning a little.

One of the police officers asked, "Are you okay, son? Can you tell me what happened?"

Ray replied, "I came in from playing outside, and George started yelling at me saying I was being loud when I came in. I said, no, I wasn't. Then he started punching me in my face and then my ribs. I begged him to stop, but he wouldn't."

One of the officers said, "I'll stay here with you and make sure you're safe while my partner questions George."

The officer went into the kitchen, where George was sitting at the kitchen table. The officer asked George, "What went on here?"

George said, "The kid was being a punk, so I set him straight."

"OK," the officer replied, "I'm going to talk to the boy's mom and see if she wants to press charges on you. Charolitte, would you like to press charges on George for striking your son?"

Charolitte replied, "No, I don't!"

"OK. We're going to have to remove your son from the household until DYS can make an evaluation and recommendation." DYS was also known as Department of Youth Services. George got to stay in the apartment and was not arrested because Ray's mom did not want to press charges. Ray was sixteen at the time of the beating. A short time later, Ray was back living under the same roof as George.

Six months later George lost the rent gambling. He said to Johnny, "I need you to give me your whole paycheck. I lost the rent money gambling."

Johnny handed over his whole paycheck to George. George asked Kathy's boyfriend, Brian, what he should do to make it up to Charolitte for losing the rent money. Brian said, "Buy her some roses."

Ray was driving his Trans Am on the highway coming from Lowell, Massachusetts, back home to Lawrence when he got pulled over by a State Trooper. Ray was driving illegally, unregistered and uninsured, because he did not have the money at the time to pay for his registration and insurance. After the state trooper pulled him over and ran his information, the trooper said to him, "Can you step out of the car, please." The trooper was a big guy, 6'5" and 250 pounds.

Ray got out of the car but did not want to get arrested, so he threw a vicious overhand right punch and knocked the state trooper out cold. Then he left the state trooper on the side of the road and jumped in his Trans Am and took off peeling out, tires screeching and smoking.

Ray returned home with his knuckles cut up, and one of them was dislocated from knocking out the state trooper. He came into the bedroom where he and his brother Johnny slept and showed Johnny what happened to his knuckles. Johnny said, "Ray, what happened to your hand?"

"I had to knock out a statey. He pulled me over and I was driving illegally. He was a big bastard too!" exclaimed Ray. "Did any stateys come to the house looking for me?" asked Ray.

"No, not yet, brother. I think you might be in the clear."
No charges were ever filed against him by the statey.

At this time, Johnny was in the middle of wrestling season, sucking weight because the coach said, "The guy at the 135 weight class isn't very good." It was the start of wrestling season, and Johnny was 165 pounds. Three weeks later he was almost down to 135 pounds. It was the day of the next meet, and Johnny still needed to lose 1 pound to make weight. So on the bus ride to the wrestling meet, Johnny put on a solar suit and ran in place in the back of the bus the whole ride to the wrestling meet. Just before they pulled up to the school, the coach said, "Johnny, get down so nobody sees you working out on the bus."

When he got to weigh-ins, Johnny got totally naked and breathed in so he could lose any once of weight to step on the scale. The opposing coach saw this and said to Johnny's coach, "What do we have here, an Olympian?"

Johnny's coach replied, "You'll see."

The wrestling meet started, and the weight class Johnny had sucked weight to get down to came and went, so he didn't think he was wrestling that day. So Johnny was being really loud and cheering on his teammates. This was an away meet, so he was annoying the fans in the stands. The coach bumped everyone up a weight class, so they then called for the 155-pound wrestlers to get on the mat. Johnny not only had to wrestle to his original weight class, but he also got bumped up a weight class because one of his teammates didn't make weight. When the 155-pound monster from the other team got on the mat, his coach said, "What are you waiting for? Grab a headgear. You're wrestling."

Johnny stepped onto the mat, and the opposing team's crowd yelled out, "Kill that little bastard!" They wrestled for the first period, but Johnny was faster since he was lighter from having to drop all that weight. Toward the end of the first period, they wrestled out of bounds close to Johnny's coach's side of the mat. Johnny's coach yelled out quick instructions. "Next time he rushes in on you, hook him up with a fireman's carry." Johnny's opponent rushed in on him, and Johnny did what the coach said and hooked him up in a fireman's carry and locked him tight in a cradle once he got him on the mat for the pin and the win. Johnny was congratulated by his coach once he got to the sidelines. And the coach said, "You better get on the bus now. This crowd wants to kill you. Don't wait till the end of the match to get on the bus." That was the last match of Johnny's senior-year season.

Shortly after wrestling season, Johnny ran away. He put all his clothes in a hockey bag and took off into the woods to his hiding place, a fort he had built in the woods. After a few nights in his hiding place, Johnny went to an apartment building and slept in the laundry room. Two days later cops found him and returned him to his apartment on Yale Street.

A few months after Johnny was returned to his apartment on Yale Street, there was another incident of violence against him perpetrated by George. Johnny was up early and could not sleep, so he was moving around doing things, making a little noise. Then he came out of his bedroom and into the hallway landing to the kitchen. George met him in the hall and punched Johnny in the face. Johnny did not go down, though. He took off out of the house and ran downtown.

This was supposed to be the morning when Johnny was going to take the test at the MEPS center to go into the marines. Johnny went downtown, and the police must have already been alerted that he had run away by his parents because they were calling out his name. "Johnny Mullen, you need to come over here to the patrol car."

Johnny ran away from the police because he did not want to be brought back home. He ran up on the roof of a car to avoid being caught by the police.

Eventually, after a long chase, the cops finally caught Johnny and handcuffed him and put him in the back of the cruiser. Johnny was seventeen at the time. The police talked to Johnny's stepdad, and he told them some bullshit lie so the police had Johnny admitted to a psychiatric hospital. After he was tested and forced to stay there for a few months, he was cleared and allowed to leave. It was determined there were no problems, and he got a note from his doctor saying there had never been any issues with Johnny and that the abusive stepdad had lied. Johnny was ordered to go see a social worker. The social worker also determined that the stepdad's abuse was the reason for Johnny's erratic behavior and running away. The social worker signed Johnny up for Social Security. It was set up so that both Johnny's name and his mother's name appeared on the check, so either one could cash it.

Once Johnny was released, he went to live with Ray and Raymond Sr. in Methuen, Massachusetts. Johnny had not been there long when his dad came after him and attacked him. His dad charged at him swinging at his head wildly. Johnny ducked his punches and got him in a bear hug and suplexed him and slammed him onto the bed. Johnny was holding his dad down, then his brother Ray came over to the bed and pulled Johnny off his dad and broke up the fight. A few months later, Johnny moved back to the apartment on Yale Street in Lawrence.

Johnny would start his senior year in high school at Greater Lawrence Tech. It was not long into his senior year that George came into Johnny's bedroom wanting to hit Johnny again. George came at him swinging. Johnny ducked his punches and put George in a half nelson. Then he forced George onto the carpeted floor and got him down to one knee. Then he knocked him flat on the floor face down and put him in a half nelson and dragged his nose across the carpet. Then Johnny locked George up in a cradle. A cradle is both hands locked and your opponent's knee pushed to their nose if you squeeze real tight, and Johnny was definitely squeezing tight.

Kathy's boyfriend, Brian, was in Johnny's bedroom watching. George said, "I am going to hit you." Brian said, after laughing, "Oh yeah? How are you going to do that? He's got you kissing your own knee." Johnny finally unlocked his grip and let George get up on his feet. George left Johnny's bedroom.

Finally, about six months later, after the outburst of violence in Johnny's bedroom, Charolitte had had enough of George's gambling and drinking relapses. She called it quits and filed for divorce.

Chapter 5

Johnny knew an older gentleman neighbor, Jerry, who was a very nice man. His sister Hellen had an apartment for rent. Johnny's mom gave her a sob story after Johnny introduced Helen to her. Helen really liked Johnny a lot, so she rented the apartment she had available on Barker Street in Methuen to his mom.

Ray also moved into Barker Street. Ray brought his then girlfriend, Lucia, with him as well. Lucia was pregnant. Johnny let his brother and his girlfriend take what would have been his bedroom, and Johnny slept on the couch. At this time Kathy was living with Brian.

While they were living on Barker Street, Charolitte started dating Dan Sullivan, a business partner of her sister Paula's husband, Jerry. After only a few months of knowing Dan, Charolitte invited him to move into the apartment on

Barker Street. He happily accepted and moved in. Charolitte did not tell her new landlord, Hellen, that Dan was moving in. She just moved him in, in the middle of the night. Hellen said to Johnny the next day, "Who is that guy? Did he move in?"

"Yes, and I'm sorry about that. My mother should have told you. His name is Dan Sullivan. My mother is so unprofessional most of the time. It's embarrassing."

"It's okay. It's not your fault, Johnny."

After living there for six months, Dan promised to buy Charolitte a house.

Ray worked for George at Healy's Appliance until there was another incident of violence. He came back to the store from a service call. A customer called Healy's Appliance and complained that Ray did not fix her appliance and left. Ray had left because when he moved the stove, he saw rats come running out at him. As soon as Ray got back to the store, George came right after Ray. George started screaming, "You are going back to that apartment." Then he went to grab Ray, and Ray knocked George out with a vicious right cross.

Johnny got back from delivering appliances to find George all messed up. Johnny asked, "What's going on here?"

Johnny's retired grandfather was working part-time repairing washers. He said, "Ray hit George and knocked him out cold!"

George was yelling, "Don't let Ray back in this store ever!"

Johnny started laughing uncontrollably. That was Ray and Johnny's last day working at Healy's Appliance. They both gladly left.

It was now a year since Dan Sullivan had promised Charolitte he would buy her a house. He finally put a bid on a house in Methuen by a golf course. The house was not ready right away. After inspection, repairs had to be done. So they had to live in a hotel for a few weeks until the new house was ready.

While they were staying in the hotel, there was an incident of nonpayment of payroll from Dan to his subcontractors. Dan had subbed out the task of plastering the latest house he was building to Mike and his crew. Mike was the boyfriend of Johnny's sister Kelly. Mike and his crew finished the job, and then, on completion of the job, Dan did not pay them. Ray was working on the crew at the time. Ray, Mike, and Chris, Mike's brother, all part of the plastering crew, went down to the hotel and met up with Johnny down at the hotel bar. The crew ran up a big bill at the bar and charged it to Dan Sullivan's room at the hotel. Mike said to Johnny while they were at the bar, "Order something. It's on Dan."

"No, thanks," Johnny replied.

After several weeks of repairs, the new house was finally ready to move into. So Charolitte, Dan, Ray, and Johnny moved into the new house, which was right next to a golf course. Lucia also moved in along with Ray's new baby boy.

A few months later, Kathy moved in because she was fighting with Brian.

After six months of living in the new house, Dan was brought up on charges of check fraud from New Mexico, and he was extradited to a New Mexico jail. Charolitte told her kids she was going to see Dan and would be back in two weeks. She never came back. Charolitte was there for a little while, established residency in New Mexico, and put in for a change of address. She ended up marrying Dan in the New Mexico prison he was being held in.

Before Johnny could receive his first Social Security check, Charolitte changed the address so the checks were sent directly to her, and Johnny never received one. She spent them for years without Johnny knowing. The only way Johnny found out about it was when he was talking to his sister Kathy, and she let it slip and said, "Thankfully, she had your Social Security checks, so when her car died, she was able to get it fixed." Years later, Johnny got a letter from Social Security saying they had overpaid him more than $3,000.00 in Social Security payments. So Johnny had to pay this back and didn't get a tax return for over three years.

The sheriff's department came knocking on the door at the house in Methuen while Charolitte was away. Johnny answered the door. The sheriff said to Johnny, "You have to vacate the premises in thirty days due to lack of payment."

Before Charolitte and Dan left for New Mexico, Charolitte came to Ray and said to him, "We need money to pay the mortgage."

So Ray, who was working at Raytheon at the time, broke his hand on purpose so he could work for Dan with a broken hand to help out with the construction of the houses that Dan was contracted to build.

When that wasn't enough money, Ray started stealing pocketbooks with his friends by driving by and snatching them from women. The police came to the house in Methuen when Johnny was home. The police officers explained to Johnny that bystanders got Ray's license plate number as people had seen him snatching pocketbooks. The police officers told Johnny that Ray needed to come down to the station for some questioning.

Ray came home from work, and Johnny told him that they had eyewitnesses placing his car at the scene of several crimes and that he needed to go down to the station for questioning. Ray went down to the police station and got questioned and worked over for hours by police until he finally cracked and said, "All right, all right. I did it. I stole those pocketbooks." He was released and given a court date for arraignment. Ray returned home to the house in Methuen.

There were only a few weeks left before they had to be out of the house. Ray found an apartment for himself, his girlfriend, his son, and Johnny. The apartment was on

Silvester Street in Lawrence. Kathy also joined them because she was once again fighting with Brian. They were not there long before Ray's arraignment date came up. Ray did not want to go to prison, so he took off to hide in Florida with his girlfriend, Lucia, and his son, Ray Ray.

Chapter 6

Kathy, Johnny, and Brian moved from Silvester Street in Lawrence to an apartment off Spit Brook Drive in Nashua, New Hampshire. Johnny got a job at a local grocery store called Market Basket. He was nineteen years old. Brian and Kathy were constantly fighting. They broke up again after living in the apartment for about a year.

Kathy and Johnny then found an apartment on Manchester Street in Nashua. They had been living there for a while when Kathy and Brian got back together again and Brian moved into their place at 32A Manchester Street. After being there for a few years, Kathy broke up with Brian and moved to North Carolina, following Charolitte, who had moved to North Carolina with Dan Sullivan once he got released from the New Mexico prison. So Johnny stayed in the apartment on Manchester Street and paid the rent by himself when Kathy took off to live with her mother and Dan Sullivan.

After not being able to get any high-paying jobs in Florida because he could not use his real name because he was on the run from the law, Ray took a job as a dishwasher. It didn't pay much at all. Ray, Ray Ray, and Lucia were staying at Lucia's uncle's down in Florida. As Ray could not make enough money to support his family, he came back to Massachusetts to face the charges he was accused of.

Ray turned himself in to the Lowell Massachusetts Police Department. Ray was processed and sent to a holding cell. After the paperwork came down, he was sent to maximum security prison to serve his time for his crimes against several citizens of Lowell.

While Ray was in prison, Raymond Sr. had a softball game through his work at Raytheon. Johnny played in the game as well. The team's name was the Longshots, and Johnny played catcher.

The game was on the line—at the end it was all tied up, 6–6. The opposing team was up in the bottom of the ninth with two outs, two strikes, and a man on second base. The pitcher wound up and delivered the pitch. It was a line shot between the third baseman and the shortstop into left field. The left fielder fielded it as it rolled to him. He came up firing to home plate as the runner that was on second base was rounding third coming home trying to score.

The throw came in from the left fielder to Johnny, who caught it on the fly just seconds before the runner trying to score got to home plate. Johnny went to apply the tag on the runner as he squared himself off. The runner tried to knock Johnny over, but the runner just bounced off him. The umpire called him safe. Johnny's teammates went nuts protesting and yelling at the umpire, as the runner was clearly out. It was the winning run for the opposing team, and the Longshots lost 7–6.

After the softball game, there was a cookout at Raymond Sr.'s boss's house. Johnny's dad proceeded to drink and get intoxicated. When it was time to head home, Johnny's dad wanted to drive, but he was way too drunk, so Johnny had to get the keys out of his hand. His dad did not want to give up the keys. So Johnny's dad swung at him, missing as Johnny ducked the wild swing of his dad's right-hand hook. Johnny got his dad in a bear hug and slammed him to the ground. Then Johnny got his dad in a half nelson with his left hand and ripped the car keys out of his hand with his right hand. Johnny said to his dad, "Now get in the car."

Johnny started driving, and his dad passed out. About an hour into the drive, his dad came to and started punching and scratching Johnny's face. Johnny could not take much more of that, so he pulled the car over and said, "If you don't stop, I'm going to knock you out cold!"

"Where are we?" asked his dad.

"I'm driving you home from the cookout."

"Oh, OK."

"Go back to sleep, and we'll be home in a half hour."

Johnny arrived at his dad's place, woke him up, and helped him up the stairs and into his bed.

Not long after this incident, Johnny took his dad to yet another rehab, as he had brought him to so many that he had lost count over the years. Sometimes Johnny would get a call from his dad after an ambulance had driven him to a rehab, and his dad would just say, "Go to my place and bring me my clothes." No hello or any sort of greeting. Just right into what he needed.

This latest time, he asked to go to Baldpate Hospital in Georgetown, Massachusetts. When he told Johnny to bring him his clothes, his dad said, "Bring me my trumpet too!"

Johnny drove up to Baldpate Hospital. It was a long, slow drive, all back roads with low speed limits.

Johnny arrived at Baldpate Hospital with all the things his dad had asked for. Johnny had to check in with the hospital staff. The staff had to go through all his dad's things to make sure there were no drugs or alcohol hidden in them. His dad came up to the staff right away and said, "Can I have my things? Give me my trumpet!" he said rudely.

"Not yet, Raymond," said the hospital staff. "I have to make sure you're not hiding any drugs or alcohol in your things."

Raymond Sr. stood there marching in place like a little child until the staff member gave him his trumpet.

Once he got his trumpet, he left Johnny standing there with the staff member and walked quickly, almost running, to the dayroom to play his trumpet. Johnny apologized to the staff member about his dad's behavior and asked if his dad could get his clothes. "After I go through them and make sure he is not hiding any drugs or alcohol in them, then I promise I will give him his clothes."

"Thank you," Johnny said to the staff member.

Then Johnny headed into the dayroom, where his father was playing his trumpet. After about five minutes, one of the staff members told Johnny's dad, "OK, Ray, you have to put your trumpet away now and play it during recreation time. I will take the trumpet for you and put it in my office. Visit with your son, who is here to see you."

"Did you bring my clothes?" Johnny's dad asked.

"Yes, I did," Johnny replied.

"Good," Raymond Sr. said. "The other patients were calling me stinky because I had no clothes to change into, and I was wearing the same clothes for a few days."

"Well, I brought up your trumpet and your clothes as soon as you called me. Did they put you on any medications?" Johnny asked.

"Yes," his dad replied. "They put me on ipecac, so if I drink, I'll throw up. And also antidepressants. Come follow me. I want to show you something." His dad led him to the recreation room, where there was an old pool table in the middle of the room. His dad was all excited. He said,

"Jackie Gleason played on this table when he was here." Then Raymond Sr. kept going on about other patients' problems and addictions during the rest of his son's visit, never focusing on his own recovery.

They walked back up to the main building from the recreation room because visiting hours were almost over. Once they got back to the main building, Johnny said, "Head into the TV room. I want to ask your doctor about your medications." But this was only a ploy for Johnny to ask his doctor other questions without his dad around. His dad headed toward the TV room.

Johnny went to his dad's doctor's office, and his door was wide open. "How can I help you?" asked the doctor.

"Is my dad ever going to get better? Is he ever going to stop drinking?"

The doctor replied, "No. He's a good old boy."

"OK. Thank you for your time, Doctor."

Johnny went into the TV room to say goodbye to his dad. "I have to go. Visiting hours are over. Call me if you need anything."

Chapter 7

While Ray was in prison, Johnny met a bunch of great people working at Market Basket Grocery Store whom he is still friends with to this very day.

Brian Dutton introduced himself to Johnny. He was very friendly. They both worked in the front end of the grocery store bagging groceries, and they both were promoted to grocery department in a short time. Johnny also met Keith, Drew, Eric Murdock, Rob Conlon, and Brian Coombes. Johnny made a bond for life with all of them.

Brian invited Johnny to his great aunt Louise's lake house up in Raymond, New Hampshire, on Governor's Lake. The two became fast friends after Johnny came up to the lake house. Keith, Brian, Eric, and Rob, a.k.a. Robbie, were all close friends. Johnny had many get-togethers that they all came to, and they had lots of laughs and so much fun together after working at Market Basket for about a year, located in the Southgate Plaza in Nashua.

Shortly after his dad got out of the treatment facility, Johnny got a call from his sister Kelly one night after working at the supermarket. Kelly said she was at Dad's house, and he was drunk and passed out again, and could he come down to Lowell and take a look at him and give her a hand? This was before Johnny had a cell phone. So if he had not gone home, he would never have gotten the message or call about his dad.

Johnny left Nashua and went to Lowell. When he arrived at his dad's apartment, he saw his dad on his side passed out on the living room carpet with coffee-ground blood chunks that his dad had thrown up. It meant that Raymond Sr. had thrown up part of his insides. Johnny went over to his dad and pulled back his eyelids, which were shut. Johnny only saw the whites of his eyes. Johnny shouted to his sister, "You idiot. He's not passed out. He's in a coma! Call a fucking ambulance!"

The EMTs got to the apartment quickly. The dad was rushed to the hospital, and his stomach was pumped to get rid of the alcohol. He was shipped from the ER to the ICU, a.k.a. intensive care unit, where he was put on a machine to keep him breathing. He had a bed that rotated to keep him from getting bedsores while he was in a coma. Kathy was a basket case. She was sleeping on the couch every night in the family waiting area. The waiting area was especially for the immediate family of ICU patients.

Ray was still in prison, and he had to fill out all kinds of paperwork with the state so he could go visit his dad at the hospital under armed guard. All of Raymond Sr.'s family visited him while he was in a coma. It was a really dramatic moment when Ray came to visit the dad in the ICU unit. Ray was with his dad in his private room and said, "You need to wake up out of this coma, so the next time I come to see you, I don't have to fill out all this paperwork again."

Johnny was just outside the room and could hear Ray talking to their dad. The nurse said, "It's good to talk to coma patients. They can hear you even though they're in a coma." All the kids were talking to their dad while he was in a coma. Their grandfather wanted to pull the plug on the breathing machine keeping him alive. Raymond Sr.'s kids said no, as they had the final say on whether the plug got pulled or not.

Seven days into his coma, Raymond Sr. miraculously came out of it. Then he was bragging about how he had been in a coma for seven days and came out of it. Even after all that and going through being in a coma, he still continued to drink.

Chapter 8

Six months after the dad came back from the hospital, Ray was released from Bridgewater State Prison. The dad and Johnny went to pick him up. Johnny drove up to Bridgewater State Prison because his dad did not have a valid driving license. Johnny arrived at the prison and went to the front desk to pick up his brother.

When Ray came out of the gates, Johnny gave him a great big bear hug. Then they quickly got out of there and walked toward the car. When they got to the car, Ray ripped off his prison T-shirt. "I couldn't wait to get out of this," he said.

Dad went on a rant about how he knew what went on at Bridgewater State Prison, yelling it at the prison guards, referencing a book written by the former screw who worked there. A screw is another name for a prison guard—a nickname. The dad has always been self-involved.

Johnny told their dad, "Be quiet and get in the car. Ray wants to get out of here. Now, shut up, and let's go!"

Their dad kept at it, yelling back at the prison. Finally, he got in the car. Johnny drove Ray back to Kelly's house. Johnny had to go to work, so he could not stay. Ray was tired and wanted to get some rest anyway. Ray wanted to see his son, Ray Ray, once he woke up. Lucia didn't let Ray see his son. Ray was furious.

During his time in prison, Ray was transferred to a work release slash transitional prison and was able to see his son then. Lucia did not let him see his son because Ray didn't make enough money at his job as a laborer for his brother-in-law Mike's plastering company to send money for child support. Ray drove his car straight into a tree at Lucia's apartment. His son was watching from the window.

About a year after Ray got out of prison, he was living at his dad's house and could not take the pressures anymore of making low money working for Mike and was sad and angry about not being able to see his kid, Ray Ray. Ray took the only course of action he thought he had left. He slit his wrists. He bled a lot into the wastebasket in the bathroom but did not bleed out and kill himself.

His friend Brian told him to save up his money and get a lawyer and get partial custody of his son. But Ray could not save up enough because there were months at a time when there was no work laboring for Mike.

Johnny found out about Ray cutting his wrists and confronted him. "Hey, Ray, what's up? Why did you cut your wrists?"

"Oh, it's nothing," Ray replied. "Don't worry about it."

Johnny said he could come work with him doing sales at Sonny's Carwash. Ray didn't want to work with the public that much. Ray and Lucia were broken up for good now.

Months later Ray was working for Mike on a job site deep in the woods and just walked off the site and disappeared into the woods. The police foot patrols, helicopters, and search dogs looked for him for a few days in those woods. When Kathy and Kelly came to Johnny's work and told him Ray had gone missing, Johnny had a bad feeling that his brother was dead. Johnny could just sense that Ray was gone.

His sister came back later in the day with the news. Kelly said to her younger brother, "We lost Ray. He's dead; the police helicopters found him. He hung himself with an extension cord from one of the trees." Ray had planned it out so that when they found him, it would be on their mother's birthday, November 8, and that was when they found him, sending a message to her that she had not been there for him in his life or his death. Kathy collapsed in Johnny's arms. He picked her up and carried her to a chair. Johnny said to Kelly, "Take Kathy home, please, and take care of her."

Chapter 9

When it came time for the funeral, Charolitte showed up late. Johnny had not seen his mother or talked to her since she left when Johnny was a teenager, when she left to marry husband number three in a New Mexico prison. Johnny was now twenty-four years old.

During the funeral service, the priest asked if anyone had any stories about Ray they wanted to share. Johnny got up and told a story about when he and Ray had a butter stick fight. They threw sticks of butter at each other. There was butter all over the walls. They both knew they were going to be in big trouble over this one! Johnny said to friends and family in attendance that they were together on that one, neither blamed the other, and both accepted the consequences. Johnny said, "I guess we just weren't together on this one." Meaning he did not want to lose his brother.

When the funeral service let out, Uncle Ray said to Johnny, "Are you even going to talk to your mother?"

Johnny turned around and hugged his mother, giving her yet another chance to be a mother. Johnny said, "I'll give you my new number. I can get a pen from Ramon's car."

Charolitte replied, "I can't wait for you to get the pen. I have to go."

Johnny couldn't believe it. He just wrote his mother off for good after she said she could not wait one minute for her son to come back with a pen. Johnny's buddy Ramon thought there was going to be a fight at the funeral between Johnny and his uncle Ray when Uncle Ray said, "You are not even going to talk to your mother."

Johnny went through an angry phase after Ray passed away. He was breaking the handles of brooms and kicking barrels. He remained angry for about a year, lashing out at people and being really short tempered. Johnny's friend Ramon helped him through this difficult time. They would hang out together at his aunt's house playing basketball or hanging out at Johnny's place. They went to the Bahama Beach Club a lot, having drinks, laughing, and dancing.

Johnny and Ramon would take turns driving. They would switch cars, and they would switch drivers. But for a week straight, they got pulled over, and the police officer would ask them, "Do you know why I pulled you over?"

Johnny would say, "No. Why did you pull us over?"

The police officer would say, "You look suspicious."

On the seventh day, they got pulled over again, and Johnny was driving. The cop asked the question again. "Do you know why I pulled you over?"

Johnny said, "No, why?"

He said again, "You look suspicious."

Johnny replied, "You've been pulling us over for a week straight. I should start to look fucking familiar."

The cop responded, "Step out of the car, please. Put your hands on the car, and spread your feet apart. I need to check you for weapons." Then he said, "Stay here on the side of the car while my partner runs your record." He came back five minutes later and said, "Your record's clean. Get out of here. You're lucky, and don't let me catch you again."

Seano was another great friend who helped him through that tough period after Ray died. Johnny and Seano would get together, make chili, have a few drinks and laughs, watch sports, and play music. They were there for each other, great friends. Johnny was there for Seano when his daughter got dropped off on his doorstep when she was only a baby and he had to raise her by himself.

Although he never lashed out at any of his friends, he lashed out at the people at work and his girlfriend at the time. Johnny left sales shortly after his brother passed away. He could not deal with the public at that time. He had become increasingly angry over his brother's passing.

Chapter 10

Johnny went to England with a good friend of his, Brian Coombes. Brian was trying to get his band, Tristan Park, signed to a record deal. Brian's relatives were from England, and he had visited England before. It was a six-and-a-half-hour flight to England. There was dense fog when they got to Heathrow International Airport, so the plane had to circle above the airport for a half hour before it could land.

It was Johnny's first time on an airplane ever. Both Brian and Johnny were excited about the possibilities of the trip. They landed, grabbed their bags, and took a taxi to Earl's Court to check into their hotel. While waiting to check into their room, Brian and Johnny were invited to go to a party. Johnny said, "Sounds good to me."

Brian said, "I'm a little wiped out from the long flight, and I want to get an early start tomorrow."

"Yeah, good idea," Johnny said. "Thank you, but we're going to have to pass on the party."

Brian and Johnny hit the ground running the next day. They got up early and went to a lot of the indie label records on a list that Brian had compiled before they left for England. Johnny and Brian used the underground, a.k.a. the subway, to get around while they were in England. The last stop on the list for dropping off Tristan Park's demo tape was Hit and Run Records. They had worked with Phil Collins and other big stars as well.

The next day Johnny and Brian went to Westminster Abby, which is a beautiful church where all the kings and queens from the past are buried; an old World War II battleship; and St. Paul's Cathedral. On Saturday they took a bus trip to Stratford-upon-Avon (Shakespeare's hometown). Brian and Johnny arrived at a bed-and-breakfast owned and run by Paul and Nina Croft, a very friendly older couple. They checked their bags in their room and then went to check out Holy Trinity Church.

Once Johnny and Brian were there, they started talking with a priest. The priest explained that in Shakespeare's time, they didn't wait long before they would knock over the headstone and put another body in the same grave after exhuming the old one and just replace the headstone. This was happening while grieving family members were still alive to visit the body they had just exhumed. So Shakespeare put a curse on his grave.

The next morning Johnny and Brian were leaving the bed-and-breakfast early. The Crofts said, "You can't stay for breakfast, boys?"

"No, we have to catch a flight back home after our bus trip back to Earl's Court."

The couple was so nice they said, "Well, here. Take a lunch." And they made Johnny and Brian a quick couple of sandwiches. It was a great trip and a good mixture of business and pleasure.

Chapter 11

They took off out of Heathrow and landed in Boston Monday afternoon. Brian returned to his band business and work. Johnny took care of some small family matters left over after Ray's passing and then took a position in manufacturing at Digital Computer Systems as a production worker, mainly building laser CAB systems and desktop systems when he started.

Eventually he learned all aspects of the plant, from assembly to shipping and receiving. It was a good move for him. At the time, Johnny was single. Six months into working at Digital, he met a girl named Monica Shelly Harper, whom he really liked a lot. She preferred to be called Shelly. Shelly and Johnny had a lot in common. They were the same age; they got along really well and became fast friends.

Johnny worked a lot of hours, so the relationship did not turn into a romantic one.

After being at Digital for about a year, Johnny became involved in a purely sexual relationship with a temp employee named Tammy, but he still had feelings for Shelly. However, things just did not work out with her. It was strictly Johnny's fault, working way too many hours at the end of each fiscal quarter. Tammy came up to Shelly and said, "Sorry I slept with Johnny."

Shelly was surprised but said, "It's okay. We're just friends." The physical relationship with Tammy ended quickly. They didn't have much in common.

Johnny started dating Barbara after the thing ended with Tammy. He had met Barbara back when he was working at the supermarket. She had blond hair and dark-brown eyes. They met working in the front end of the store. Barbara was a cashier, and Johnny was a bagger. They would go back to Johnny's place and drink Bud Lights. They also hung out with mutual friends at the supermarket and went to the dance club the Bahama Beach Club. The relationship lasted for seven months. Then they remained friends after the relationship ended.

Barbara brought over her friend Kim to Johnny's place. He had just gotten out of the shower when Barbara knocked on his door. Johnny answered the door with only a towel wrapped around him. Johnny said to them, "Hey, come on in. Would you like a drink? Have a seat, please."

Kim told Barbara later after they left Johnny's place that she was into him, and she asked Barbara for his number. Barbara gave Kim Johnny's number.

Later that evening Kim called Johnny to set up a date. Johnny said, "Come over to my place at seven o'clock, and we can plan our night from there."

When Kim got to Johnny's place, she knocked on the door. Johnny came to the door and said, "Nice to see you again. Come on in and have a seat on the couch." He asked her, "Would you like something to drink?"

She replied, "Yes."

Johnny said, "All I have is Bud Light. Is that okay?"

She said, "Yes."

He gave her a bottle of beer and lit the candles on the coffee table.

After forty minutes of getting to know each other, he excused himself to check on the dinner he was cooking for her. Dinner was ready. Johnny set the table and laid out all the food in serving dishes. He came back out into the living room and said to Kim, "Dinner is ready. Follow me."

They ate dinner, then Johnny took Kim by the hand and led her to the couch and started to gently kiss her on her neck. Then he moved over to her lips, kissing her passionately and deeply. Then he took her hand and slowly walked her to his bedroom, where they made love all night long until sunrise.

When the morning light came streaming through Johnny's bedroom window, he looked over at the candles that he had lit at the start of their lovemaking and saw that they were burnt all the way down to nothing. Kim woke up and rolled over to look at Johnny and kissed him on the lips ever so softly and said to him, "I have to head home; I have to get to work after I shower."

For the first month, it was really good between Kim and Johnny. But during week five, things started to take a turn for the worse. Kim brought up a former drug habit she had failed to mention when she first started seeing Johnny.

There was an episode that she had at Denny's Restaurant. She was very belligerent and high on street drugs and alcohol. She lashed out at him in a high and drunken tirade in a Denny's Restaurant. She was with another guy, and she said, "I think it's love." The next day she didn't remember the prior evening's events.

For two weeks Johnny didn't even want to talk to her. He finally called her and told her what she had said in her drug-and-alcohol-induced state. She could not believe it. She was totally clueless about what had happened. When they finally talked in person several weeks later, Johnny said, "It's over between us, and I don't want to see you again."

Several weeks later Kim called Johnny saying he needed to come over because a pregnancy test she took came up positive. He said, "Wait there. I'll be right over, and we'll go to the hospital and have your doctor give you a pregnancy test." When Johnny got to Kim's house, she wasn't there. Her sister told Johnny she had gone out to the store.

She returned from the store, and they went to the hospital to take a pregnancy test. They called up for the test results and were told she was not pregnant. The relationship with Kim was beyond repair, so they split for good.

Chapter 12

It was St. Patrick's Day, and Johnny was celebrating with his buddy Rich at Strangebrew Bar and Grill in Manchester, New Hampshire. A friend of Johnny's, Brian Carr, met up with them at Strangebrew. Johnny ordered the first round of drinks. He ordered black and cherries. Black and cherries are a mixture of Guinness and Sam Adams cherry wheat. "These are so tasty," remarked Johnny. There was a live band there playing Irish songs. They were all enjoying the music and the infectious atmosphere.

After a couple of drinks, Johnny and Rich said goodbye to Brian. They wanted to get closer to home, so they went to Johnny's place and left his car in his parking lot and walked to the pub close to Johnny's place, where he was friends with the owners. The place was packed. Rich and Johnny walked up to the bar, and Johnny's buddy Dan was tending bar. He was also one of the two owners.

Dan had seen Johnny walking up to the bar over the crowd of people. Dan signaled to Johnny, How many drinks do you want? Johnny signaled two drinks by holding up two of his fingers. Dan brought over the two drinks, and Johnny said, "Thank you. How are you, buddy?"

"Busy," Dan replied. "How have you been?"

"I'm hanging in there," Johnny replied. It was pretty noisy in there, so they had to shout at each other to be heard because the drums and bagpipes were playing. Johnny loved the sound of bagpipes.

When Johnny grabbed the drinks, he looked to his left and noticed a beautiful woman. She had long, black, curly hair and a beautiful smile to match her stunning looks. Johnny said, "Hi. Happy St. Paddy's Day. My name is Johnny."

She replied, "Nice to meet you. My name is Brunilda."

Johnny reached out and shook her hand. He said, "This is my buddy Rich."

"Nice to meet you, Rich," she replied.

"How is your St. Paddy's Day going?" asked Johnny.

"I'm bored," she said.

Johnny was attracted to her right away. "Where are your friends?" he asked.

"I don't have any friends" she said sarcastically. "I moved here from New Jersey."

"Jersey girl," he said. "I like Jersey girls," he said to Bruni. "If you want, I can ask a friend of mine, Lisa, if she needs another team member for her bowling team."

She said, "Sure."

Johnny said, "OK, give me your cell phone number."

Bruni said "OK" and gave Johnny her number. He saved it in his phone.

Johnny called Bruni to let her know that Lisa said they didn't need another player for their team.

"That's OK," Bruni said. "You know something?"

Johnny replied, "What?"

"The other night when we met, I wanted to kiss you."

Johnny said, "Well, come get your kiss right now. My address is twenty-eight Birch Street."

She arrived at his place two minutes later because she lived right down the street from him.

Johnny heard a knock on the door. He opened the door and it was Bruni standing there. He invited her in. "Come on in," said Johnny. He shut and locked the door behind her. Then he started kissing her passionately. Then, after a few minutes of deep, passionate kissing, he picked her up off her feet and carried her to his bedroom.

He started kissing Bruni with lots of passion and intensity. Then they started tearing each other's clothes off. Johnny started kissing her lips softly and sensuously. Then he moved slowly to her neck, kissing the right side of her neck just below her right earlobe and nibbling on her ear for just a little while. Then he started kissing her all up and down her neck.

He slowly moved down to her stomach, giving her soft, sensuous kisses all over her belly. Then Johnny gently opened up her legs and started kissing her inner thighs slowly and taking his time moving inwards toward her sacred place, and he started pleasuring her. She began to breathe deeply and moan with pleasure. Then he put his tongue deep inside her. She gasped and grabbed his head and pulled it closer to her, digging her long nails into the back of his head. Then she lifted his head and told him to get on his back. Then she took him into her mouth and started pleasuring him.

It was not long before Johnny could not take any more and had to have her. He said to her, "Stop," and she looked up at him and stopped. He said to her, "Get on top of me." He started rocking her back and forth once she got on top of him. She really started to get into it and the rhythm of the rocking, and she started to grind herself on him really deep and really hard. Her whole body shook as she orgasmed. They made love till four in the morning.

Bruni would come over at four thirty in the morning before Johnny went to work to make love to him. They would make love for hours then kiss, and both would head off to work. One night Johnny went to a Red Sox game with his buddy Brian and came back around one thirty in the morning. Johnny left the door unlocked, as he did a lot while he was seeing Bruni, so she could come on in on those early mornings and let herself in.

At around three thirty that morning, Johnny heard his door open and close again. He heard two voices, both of them women. Johnny could hear them talking in his living room just outside his bedroom. Bruni came into Johnny's bedroom and said, "Don't try and pretend you're sleeping."

Johnny replied, "Nope. I was trying to sleep earlier, but I couldn't, so I'm just lying here."

"I brought a new friend." Bruni had met her out at a local restaurant.

Brian and Johnny at Red Sox game

Bruni went back out into the living room where her new friend was waiting and walked her into Johnny's bedroom. Bruni said to Johnny, "You can't touch right now. You have to watch first before you can touch."

The two girls started kissing each other while Johnny sat in a chair in his bedroom and watched for like five minutes. Then he could not wait any longer.

Johnny walked up to Bruni, took off her shirt, and then took off the shirt of Bruni's new friend, Erica. He then took off Bruni's pants and then Erica's. The girls stripped off their bras and panties. Both of the girls got on the bed. Erica lay flat on her back while Bruni started kissing her again. Then Johnny took all his clothes off and pulled Bruni off Erica and started taking her from behind. Erica got off the bed and started watching them while she pleasured herself. Erica said to Bruni, "Is he fucking you good?"

Bruni, in a low, sexy voice, replied, "Yes, he is."

Then Erica got back on the bed, lying on her back while Johnny pleasured her at the same time Bruni was kissing Erica. Then he flipped Erica around so she was on all fours on his bed. Then he pulled her close and started to pleasure her from behind.

The hour was getting late. Erica said, "We have to get home. It's really late. Sweet dreams, Johnny." Both girls left blowing kisses as they exited Johnny's bedroom.

Bruni had found this new friend of hers on Johnny's request. She had asked him, "What do you want?"

Rich,Johnny and Brian at Red Soxs' game

Johnny told her, "I want a threesome." She was very adventurous sexually. She liked to experiment. Johnny experimented with a lot of things sexually during the four months they were together. She liked to be whipped with a belt and dominated. She also liked to be choked and spanked. She got really turned on when he ripped her panties right off her body, leaving a small mark across her leg.

The day he did that, she texted him saying, "I can't stop looking at the mark on my leg. It's making me hot and horny. I want more" she said.

Eventually, though, things fizzled out, and it ended. She was too up and down with her moods. It ended civilly, and they wished each other well.

Johnny was hanging out with Stacy as friends while seeing Bruni. One afternoon at Stacy's house, she took Johnny's car keys and said, "If you were not in a relationship, I would make you earn getting your car keys back" as she put his car keys behind her back, allude to having sex with Johnny. Then she put the car keys down her pants. Once it was officially over with Bruni, Johnny started dating Stacy. It was only a few weeks after she had said she would make him earn his keys back.

Chapter 13

Johnny had signed up to join the army a few months before he had started dating Stacy, so he only had a month to spend with her before he shipped out to basic training. Stacy had stated, "It's not fair. We just started dating, and now you're going away to the army, and I won't be able to see you."

Johnny started basic training seven weeks before Christmas. So at Christmastime he was able to go back home for Christmas exodus. Two of Johnny's best friends picked him up at the airport, Brian and Keith. They picked him up in Brian's Camaro.

On the first stop, they went to Market Basket, where Johnny used to work, to pick up some beer and say hi to some old friends who still worked there. Johnny said hi to an old boss, and then a friend of Johnny's, Karen Martinelli, came over and said hi. Karen said, "You look good in your uniform."

"Thank you. You look good yourself," Johnny remarked.

Keith, Johnny, and Brian were going to the Bahama Beach Club Thursday night, just two days away, to have a few drinks and do some dancing. So Johnny said to Karen, "You should go to the Bahama Beach Club this Thursday." Things had already ended with Stacy. Karen smiled and said, "I'll be there."

Thursday night, Keith showed up at Brian's, where Johnny was staying, to pick him up to head to the Bahama Beach Club. Keith and Johnny went to the club together. Their buddy Brian went in a separate car and came with his girlfriend, Melanie. Keith and Johnny got to the club first. They went up to the bar. They knew the bartender, Joyce, so they got taken care of pretty well. "Hi, Joyce. How have you been?" Johnny said.

"OMG, Johnny. Where have you been?"

"I've been at basic training for the army."

She came over and gave Johnny a hug. Keith and Johnny had a couple of Alabama Slammers while they were waiting for their buddy Brian to get there. Brian arrived about an hour later with Melanie. Joyce got all of them a round of Alabama Slammers.

After a couple of drinks, Johnny started dirty dancing with Karen. Both were really getting into it. After they had been drinking and dancing for a while, the bouncer came over and asked Johnny to leave because he thought Johnny had had one too many drinks. He escorted Johnny to the door.

Johnny went outside, and Brian followed him out. Brian wanted Johnny to come home with him and his girlfriend. Johnny wanted to stay and wait for Karen and Keith to come out of the club. Johnny found the keys to Keith's car under the hood scoop. It was really cold outside, so Johnny started up the car and got in the back seat to fall asleep and wait for Keith and Karen to come out of the club.

While he was lying down in the back seat and waiting for Karen and Keith, a cop came up to the car and opened the door after knocking on the window. The cop asked Johnny to step out of the vehicle. He gave Johnny a sobriety test. He failed it, and then the cop arrested him.

A week later Johnny had to go back to Fort Knox to finish his basic training. He had to let his commanding officer know about his run-in with the Nashua police. Johnny looked into getting a JAG lawyer once he got back to Fort Knox. The army lawyers told Johnny that JAG didn't represent DWI cases. JAG stands for judge advocate general. Three weeks later Johnny graduated from basic training and was shipped to AIT, Advanced Individual Training.

A few months later, Johnny had to come back home to face the DWI charges. He hired a lawyer in his hometown. Johnny and his good friend Keith entered the courtroom. Keith testified on Johnny's behalf, and his buddy Brian also took the stand in defense of Johnny. The trial concluded, and Johnny was found not guilty—which was justice because Johnny had no intention of driving. But the damage done was unrepairable. Johnny's career in the military was finished. He was already out of the army on a discharge before the trial started.

Chapter 14

Johnny took a job in sales through a friend of his. He excelled and became top salesman for his location. When Johnny came back from the service, he and his friends started having weekend ski trips. Before that, the group of friends was taking weekend trips to Maine in the summertime. One of Johnny's friends, Eric, had a cabin in Maine, which overlooked a picturesque lake.

The group of six guys, sometimes seven, would head up in two cars on Friday nights in the summertime. They would alternate in the summer months between going to Eric's camp in Maine and Brian's camp on Governor's Lake in Raymond, New Hampshire. Both camps had canoes and boats. They would play wallyball. Wallyball is a version of volleyball that they had come up with. It's just like volleyball except the ball can only bounce once. There was a motorboat up at Brian's camp, and he had all the toys to pull behind it, like a tube, a kneeboard, water skis, and a scurfer. Johnny liked tubing and knee boarding the most, of the water sports that the group did. And Johnny loved playing wallyball.

At nighttime they sat around the campfire. It was so peaceful at night sitting around the campfire sharing stories and now and then, looking up at the sky and gazing at the

Seano,Brian,Keith,rich,and Johnny at Red Sox game celebrating 2013 Red Soxs championship

stars. Night faded into early morning, and Johnny put out the fire and headed off to sleep.

If it was a weekend when the group of friends was at the camp up in Maine, the next day after getting up there late Friday night, Johnny and his buddies would wake up and head to the golf course in Madison and play eighteen holes of golf. They would arrive at the course and unload their bags. It was a really scenic setting at the golf course. They would check in at the pro shop and sign in as guests and pay for the eighteen holes of golf.

Then, because it was a tradition of theirs, they would go to the restaurant side and have a hot dog and a beer. Johnny and his buddies would say, "Hi, how have you been?" to the lady running the restaurant side of the golf shop. She had been working there for many years. Johnny and his friends got to know her from their trips to the camp over the years.

After their traditional hot dog and beer, they would jump in the golf cart and hit the course, laughing and talking about the past and playing golf, hitting good shots and bad—but laughing at the bad shots and when they missed the ball entirely on a swing. Not taking it too seriously, just having fun enjoying one another's company.

After they finished playing eighteen holes, they headed back to the camp. Eric, one of Johnny's best friends, sparked the grill. Johnny grabbed the burgers and the chicken out of the fridge and brought them out to Eric, who was still by the grill. After they ate, Johnny and the boys took off in the canoes to tour the lake. It was starting to get late, so they headed back to the cabin to start a fire just before nightfall. They grabbed all the chairs and put them in a circle surrounding the fire they had just started.

The boys started telling stories about the old times and cracking jokes at one another's expense. But not with malicious intent. They drank through the night socially, and Saturday night became Sunday morning, so Johnny and his buddy Eric put out the fire, as they were the last two who had not gone to sleep yet. After they put out the fire, Johnny and Eric said, "Good night. See you later today." Laughter followed their comments.

On Sunday morning everyone woke up, cleaned up the camp, and packed up their things for their journey back home to Massachusetts. Before they headed back home, Eric made breakfast for everyone, which consisted of Eric, Johnny, and Wayne, Eric's brother.

After they had returned home to Massachusetts, Johnny received a call from one of his best friends, Keith, inviting him to dinner at his house on Monday night. Johnny's buddy Wade was invited as well. Johnny arrived at Keith's house just before Wade. Wade arrived minutes later. Keith was living with his girlfriend, Shannon. Keith said, "Have a seat. I have something to tell you." Johnny and Wade sat down. Keith said, "Shannon and I are getting married!"

Johnny replied, "Wow! Congratulations!"

Wade said sarcastically, "Good luck!"

This announcement came shortly after Keith and Shannon moved into their new home together. Keith's parents were not happy with this development. They thought they were getting married too soon after they just bought their new home. With a house payment and then having to pay for a wedding, they thought it was too much in a short time period.

It was a nice ceremony. All of Keith's and Shannon's friends and family were in attendance. Everyone went to the reception after the ceremony. Keith and his friends were having so much fun at the reception that Keith's parents paid for an extra hour to keep it going. Keith and Shannon and all their close friends were having so much fun dancing, drinking, and laughing.

The night came to an end, and everybody went off to their hotel rooms to get some sleep. The next morning Keith and Shannon were leaving for their honeymoon. Johnny and Brian were waving and shouting goodbye and having fun from their hotel window.

The next member of the tight group of friends to get married was Brian. He married Becky, a nurse in training. Originally Brian had blown her off on the first date they were supposed to go, set up by another friend's wife. Rashid's wife set up the date. Brian talked with Johnny about blowing her off. Brian said to Johnny, "Should I call her?"

Johnny replied, "Yes, you should call her. Say you're sorry; a family emergency came up."

Brian eventually called to reschedule the date. They went out on their date, and a little over a year later, they got married.

Wade was the next member of the group to get married. He married Karen, one of Sofia's friends. Sofia was a friend of Wayne, one of Johnny's buddies. Karen and Wade met on a ski trip. Holly, Sofia's friend, organized the ski trip. Holly had a ski trip at Sugarloaf Mountain in Maine every winter. Wade and Karen dated for a while and then tied the knot.

About a year after the ski trip when Karen and Wade met, Shannon and Keith had their first child, Amanda. Johnny and his friends went to the hospital to congratulate Keith and Shannon. Shortly after Amanda was born, Johnny's dad died.

Chapter 15

Just a few years earlier, Ray had passed away. Raymond Sr. passed away in his chair with half a gallon of whiskey on either side of him. Five years later, Johnny's nephew Michael passed away. He was found by the dumpster. He was taking opioids. It was a really sad funeral. Such a shame to see a young kid of twenty-three die who was full of potential and promise. He died just like his uncle Ray in the sense that he passed away too young.

Michael had said to his uncle Johnny that when he had trouble getting home, he would stop at the cemetery and see his uncle Ray's grave and ask for his uncle's help in getting him home safely. Michael's uncle Ray was only twenty-five when he passed away.

Not long after Michael passed away, his dad was in a horrific motorcycle accident. He got really intoxicated and drove head-on into a fire truck. He was in a coma for about a week. The doctors had to put a metal plate in his head and pins and rods in his legs. He now takes pain pills and still drives after drinking.

The police did not charge him with DWI (driving while intoxicated) when he drove into the fire truck. But after he was all healed up, he was driving after drinking too much, and the police pulled him over and arrested him and charged him with two DWIs—one for hitting the fire truck and one for this most recent incident he was being arrested for. He walks with a limp and a cane now, a reminder to himself of his own stupidity.

Earlier on the day of the crash, he visited his daughter Michelle drunk and out of his mind. She was worried about him; he left swerving all over the road. He operated his life with no regard to anyone's feelings whatsoever.

Once he was fully recovered, Kelly finally left him and his destructive ways. At this time Kelly was in recovery from drugs and alcohol—drugs and alcohol that he had introduced her to when she was only sixteen years old. She had been clean for a while and in a program with a support system. About a year into recovery, Kelly started dating someone in the program. The nice man she met was Ken. The two eventually got married after a courtship.

Chapter 16

Johnny was supposed to walk Kelly down the aisle and give her away, but he was in the hospital the day of her wedding. Johnny had become ill from the chemicals he worked with. He had joint and muscle pain. He was also itchy. His New Hampshire primary care doctor prescribed a steroid called prednisone. After Johnny had been taking the steroid for a short time, the doctor increased the dosage to try to get rid of his symptoms.

On the first day of the increase, Johnny had severe pain on both sides of his body, he had trouble breathing, and his right foot swelled up so much, he had trouble putting on his shoe. Johnny decided to lie down on his bed, hoping things would get a little better with time. But things only got worse. His airway was closing fast.

He called his girlfriend, Gina, and asked her to come over just to make sure he wouldn't stop breathing. Gina got to Johnny's place really fast. She came flying up his steps, as he lived on the second floor. Johnny had left his apartment door unlocked, as he was a little out of it from the medication he was taking. He would have normally locked his door. Gina came bursting through the front door and went straight for Johnny's bedroom, where he was lying motionless on his bed.

She opened his bedroom door and said, "Pick a hospital."

Johnny replied, "Just leave me here on the bed."

She said, "You're going. Just pick a hospital."

Johnny was too weak to fight her. He said "Parkland Hospital, I guess. It's the closest. Both of my sides are in a lot of pain. Can you help me get out of bed?"

Gina grabbed ahold of his arms and pulled him up enough so he could sit up on the side of the bed. She had to help him get dressed. Johnny's right foot was so swollen, Gina could barely put his shoe on. She just put it on loosely and didn't tie it. She put Johnny's arm around her shoulder and walked him down the stairs and put him in her car.

They arrived at the hospital emergency entrance, and Gina walked Johnny in. The emergency staff asked a few quick questions, and then they took Johnny right into a room and hooked him up to an IV. Gina followed Johnny into the room and stayed by his side. The medication they pumped in through the IV opened up his airway. They kept

Johnny overnight for observation. Gina went home to get some rest.

The next afternoon the hospital released Johnny. Shannon, Keith's wife, was in the parking lot when Johnny got out. She was upset that the hospital had released Johnny so soon. She said to Johnny, "Are you okay to be released?"

Johnny replied, "Yes, I feel OK."

Shannon hugged him and cried.

Johnny said, "I'm going to head to Robbie's house for his fortieth birthday party. I have to go pick up a new phone and a gift for Robbie."

Robbie was one of Johnny's best friends. He had known him since he was nineteen years old.

After Johnny picked up a gift for Robbie he could not remember how to get to Robbie's or how to get back to his own apartment. Johnny called Shannon after he was driving around for hours lost. Shannon picked up her phone and Johnny said, "It's me, Johnny. I can't remember how to get home."

Shannon said, "Can you find Market Basket, where we worked as teenagers together?"

"Yes, I think so," Johnny said.

Shannon said, "Stay there, and Keith and I will come get you."

Keith drove Johnny to the hospital, and Shannon followed them in Johnny's car. They checked Johnny into the emergency room at Southern New Hampshire Medical in Nashua. The doctor came into the examination room. Johnny was there with Shannon; Becky, Brian's wife; Wayne; and Keith. Johnny could barely speak. The doctor said he was going to give Johnny an epidural shot in his lower back.

Wayne left the exam room because he was afraid of needles. The doctor said, "Are you ready?"

Johnny, being out of it, heard "lower back," so he got up on all fours on the exam table and ended up mooning the entire waiting room.

The doctor said, "No, just lie on your stomach." It was a huge needle. The doctor said, "This may take a while to go all the way in." The shot was to make sure there was no damage happening to the brain.

Johnny was transferred up to a regular room eventually, and all his friends went home. That night while Johnny was in his hospital bed he started having severe shooting pains in his back. He hit the button to call the nurse on duty into his room and told her of his severe pain. She relayed it to his doctor, and Johnny was given drugs to take the pain away. All his friends came to see him while he was in the hospital.

After a few days, Johnny was released from the hospital and was told once again to follow up with his primary care physician. His primary care physician continued to prescribe prednisone. Johnny seemed to be getting continually worse. After working a twelve-hour shift and taking his dose of prednisone, Johnny could not sleep and felt really strange. He was hallucinating, seeing relatives who had passed on.

Johnny left his apartment early that morning walked down Birch Street and headed toward West Broadway. On West Broadway, he broke into a car. He did not stay in it long, and he left his cell phone in it. He walked to the Irish pub Halligans and, not realizing what time of day it was, pulled on the door and tried to go in.

Then he got back on West Broadway Street, walked a little ways, and broke into a house he mistook for his grand-father's house. An older gentleman came out of his shower to find Johnny just standing there in his living room. The older gentleman said, "Just take my money."

Johnny did not take it.

The older man said, "I'm calling the police. Wait here."

Johnny stood right outside the gentleman's house, in his driveway, waiting for the police to arrive.

Two cops arrived on the scene, one a very beautiful woman and the other well-built man. They asked Johnny for his name and address and asked him what he was doing there. Johnny only gave his first name every time he was asked the question, nothing else.

The male police officer said, "We can't help you if you don't give us the info we're asking you for."

Johnny finally told him, "Johnny Mullen. I live at twenty-eight Birch Street, apartment two."

The police officer relayed his info through his handheld radio. They dispatched a unit to Johnny's apartment to try to get more info. A unit went over to Johnny's place and talked to his roommate, Alicia. Alicia said, "Johnny was acting really strange." He had said to her over and over again, "I don't feel right." The info got relayed from the unit at Johnny's place to the arresting officers on the scene. The male officer handcuffed Johnny and put him in the back of the police car.

The officers drove him to the station booked him and put him in a holding cell until they could figure out what to do with him. The cop kept saying to Johnny, "Are you on anything? Did you take any drugs?"

Johnny kept replying, "No. Go fuck yourself!"

The cop finally said, "All right, we're taking you to the hospital." They transported Johnny to the hospital.

Once they arrived, they set him up in a bed in the emergency room under the watch of two policemen. Johnny's buddy Keith was there with Johnny in his room. A security guard kept getting in Johnny's face. Keith said, "Please, I know you think you're tough, but if you don't back off, he's going to hurt you and a few others and end up in jail. So please just look away and leave him alone."

So the security guard backed off and stopped staring Johnny down.

The nursing staff kept asking Johnny to give them a urine sample, but Johnny kept refusing them. The nurse said to him, "If you don't, we're going to have to put a tube in your penis and take the urine sample." The nurse told Keith you have to leave the room. The nurse called a bunch of people to hold Johnny down while she inserted the tube inside his penis. They wanted to test to see if he was on any drugs.

Eventually they transferred Johnny upstairs to a regular room, and the test came back negative—no drugs. Just the prednisone his doctor had prescribed. After a few days, they released Johnny. He had a court date for the breaking and entering. Johnny decided to give up on the New Hampshire doctors. He went to stay at his friend Wayne's house and headed to Massachusetts General to see if they could figure out the health problems he was having.

Johnny took the train to Massachusetts General first thing Monday morning. The emergency room at Massachusetts General ran a bunch of tests and then set up an appointment for Johnny to be seen at the allergy department. He got his appointment with the allergy doctor, Dr. Dutta. Johnny's new doctor had already gone through the transferred patient information on Johnny from his New Hampshire doctors.

Johnny went to the appointment with Dr. Dutta. Dr. Dutta introduced herself to Johnny. "Hi, I'm Dr. Dutta. Nice to meet you." She extended her hand.

Johnny said, "Hi, nice to meet you" and shook her hand.

She said, "I'm just going over your file, and I need to ask you some questions. So you have joint and muscle pain?"

"Yes," Johnny answered.

"I see you have circular raised hives. Your New Hampshire doctors have you on prednisone, a steroid."

"Yes," Johnny replied. "But I can't take prednisone anymore. I found out I'm allergic to it. They said I had a steroid-induced psychosis."

"They?" Dr. Dutta asked.

"Yes, the doctors at Southern New Hampshire Medical Center."

"OK, Mr. Mullen," Dr. Dutta replied. "I'm going to put you on a couple of different medications to try and get your symptoms under control. You'll have to come see me twice a month at first, then I will drop it to once a month after we get things under control."

For months the doctor treated Johnny, but his symptoms persisted. The doctor mentioned to Johnny injections that she thought would help him a great deal. She submitted that she recommended Zolair injections for him. Johnny received paperwork from his insurance company saying they would not pay for Zolair injections. Johnny went to his next doctor's appointment and let Dr. Dutta know the insurance company would not cover the cost of the injections. Dr. Dutta said, "That's OK. I can submit paperwork for a foundation to pay for the injections. You just have to fill out the paperwork and return it to me. It's called the Access to Care Foundation."

"Thank you, Dr. Dutta. I appreciate all your help." Johnny filled out the paperwork and returned it to her.

A little over a week later, it was approved, and Johnny was able to start the Zolair injections. The hives went away, but the muscle and joint pain was still a constant thing for him. Johnny continued the injections for four years. In that time he went to his court date for breaking and entering when he had the allergic reaction to the steroids and broke into a car and a house.

Before court was in session, Johnny went to the prosecutor's office and showed him the paperwork from the doctors at Southern New Hampshire Regional. The paperwork stated Johnny had steroid-induced psychosis. Johnny said he just wanted to be done with this and not go to trial. The prosecutor said, "I can give you community service until fines that will be accessed are paid."

When Johnny's case was called, the prosecutor approached the bench saying, "We have already come to an agreement, Your Honor."

"Mr. Mullen, are you representing yourself?"

"Yes, Your Honor, I am. I have paperwork from my doctors stating that I had steroid-induced psychosis."

The judge said to Johnny, "You do understand the burden of proof is on the state to prove you were in your right state of mind when you committed these crimes?"

"Yes, Your Honor. I just want to be done with this right now so I can focus on my health."

"OK, son," the judge replied.

The judge wanted Johnny to bring it to trial because he knew Johnny would win, since he had not been in his right state of mind because of the allergic reaction to the steroids.

A deal was reached; case closed; next case.

Johnny completed his community service hours and began to get healthier along the way.

Every once in a while, Kelly would give updates on Charolitte to Johnny. The latest one was that her husband, Dan Sullivan, had a whole other family. He would go see them on holidays—married to Charolitte and having another relationship with another woman. Charolitte found out and ended their marriage. She was so embarrassed, she changed her name to Gene Lebranch. Johnny would always say to Kelly, "Why do you still talk to her? Please don't give me any more updates on your mother. I don't want to hear them anymore!"

Johnny went back to work with the help of Dr. Dutta and the Zolair injections. He was working at Velcro. He still had joint and muscle pain, but the hives were completely gone. It was a rough first month back, but Johnny pushed through it. It was good to get back to work. Too much time on your hands can be troublesome to the mind. Too much time to ponder and overthink every little thing.

Johnny started to feel a little better after that first month back at work. He kept up with his Zolair injections and doctor visits for four years. Then Dr. Dutta released Johnny from her care but left the Zolair injection order open in case symptoms came back. Johnny started getting back to hiking and all the things he enjoyed doing before he got sick, like golfing, playing volleyball at the lake house, and, of course, going to Red Sox games. Johnny definitely had a great appreciation for life and the people in it who cared for him so much.

When Johnny got sick, he truly saw how many amazing people were in his life and how much love they had for him. He told all his friends and family how much he loved them with more frequency and with an open heart full of love and caring for them.

Chapter 17

Johnny reconnected with his old buddy Sully, a.k.a. Sean Sullivan, through social media. Johnny had to move away from Sully and all his friends in Pawtucketville. He did not even get the chance to say goodbye to any of them. None of Johnny's friends knew what had happened to him. Just one day Johnny was gone.

Johnny found Sully on a site that had McAve Junior High. Johnny had seen the group and searched to see if Sully was a part of it. As luck would have it, he was, so Johnny sent Sully a message: "Hey, Sully, it's Johnny Mullen. How are you?"

Sully responded, "OMG is that little Johnny Mullen?"

"Yeah, buddy, it's me."

"How have you been?" Sully asked.

"I've been great, buddy. How about you?"

"I'm doing well," Sully replied.

Johnny said, "We should get together for some drinks sometime and catch up."

Sully replied, "Absolutely! I'm working with my wife, Cheryl, bartending at Finn's Pub on Sundays. Come on down."

"OK, sounds great, buddy. Looking forward to seeing you."

Sunday came, and Johnny went down to Finn's Pub, located in downtown Lowell, Massachusetts. Johnny came into Finn's Pub, and there was a blonde woman tending bar. Johnny said to her, "Is Sully here?"

"Yeah, he's in the bathroom," she replied.

Sully came out of the bathroom saying, "I heard somebody call my name." Then he saw Johnny. "OMG, you're taller now. I didn't think you would show," Sully exclaimed. He gestured over to the blond woman bartending. "This is my wife, Cheryl."

"Hi. I'm Johnny."

"Sit down. Have a seat. Wow, Johnny Mullen out of the woodwork. I can't believe you made it. Where have you been? What have you been up to, Johnny? We all wondered what happened to you and Ray. One day you were just gone."

"My mother and my stepdad, George, moved us to Lawrence, Massachusetts, at Christmastime, and they didn't let us say goodbye to anyone."

Sully asked Johnny, "Is Ray gone?"

Johnny lowered his head in sadness and said, "Yeah, Ray's dead."

"How did he go?"

"He hung himself with an extension cord when he was on a job site. He took off on his morning break and went deep in the woods on the job site and hung himself with an orange extension cord."

"Sorry to hear that, buddy."

"Yeah, Ray was in a lot of physical and emotional pain."

"Where are you living these days, Johnny?"

"Derry, New Hampshire. How about you, Sully?"

"I'm over in Hudson, New Hampshire."

"Oh, nice. Hudson is a nice town," Johnny said.

"How are you liking Derry?"

"It's nice and quiet. Do you still see anybody from the old Pawtucketville neighborhood?" Johnny asked.

"Yeah. I went and saw Scott Draper's band a few times, and I still keep in touch with Marcus Reyes and Heath Gaffeney."

"That's awesome! How are all those guys doing?"

"They're doing great! Marcus runs his own fitness company, and Heath owns his own company. Scott Martin is doing well too."

"That's great. I haven't seen all those guys in years. I miss those guys—all great people! We'll have to get together with everybody from the old neighborhood."

"Yes, definitely," Sully replied. "We can try to organize a reunion."

"Sounds great. Count me in," Johnny said.

Sully's shift at the bar ended, so he came around the other side of the bar to have a few drinks with Johnny and continue catching up with his old friend. Sully said to his wife, "The girls at McAve Junior High loved this little guy."

"Yeah, probably because I was so short. I didn't date any of them. There was too much to deal with inside my house to invite any girl into that nightmare. I liked them too much to want to subject them to that nightmare that went on inside my house. So what's going on with you, Sully? What have you been up to?"

"I work at New Penn Trucking full-time driving a rig and bartend part-time, and I clean the Glenview once a week in the morning"

"Wow. Busy man."

"Oh yeah, I am. Cheryl and I have two boys, all grown up."

"Very cool," Johnny said. "How long have you guys been married?"

"Twenty years" Sully replied.

"That's awesome," Johnny said. "Pretty much right out of high school then?"

"Yeah, pretty much. Well, we have to head home, Johnny. Four thirty Monday morning comes early."

"I hear you, buddy. It was great to see you again and catch up."

"Absolutely, Johnny. We'll have to get together again real soon."

"Sounds great to me," Johnny replied. "I'll give you my cell phone number."

"OK, cool. Talk to you soon, Johnny. I'll walk you out. Where are you parked?"

"I'm right on the side of the street by the old Woolworth's."

"OK, cool. Great to see you again. Drive safe, Johnny."

Johnny got back home and was in such a good mood after reconnecting with his old friend Sully.

A few months later, Sully and Johnny got back together again and met up for drinks and appetizers. They caught up on what was going on in each other's lives. Johnny said, "Hey, baseball season is coming up soon. We should catch a Red Sox game together."

"Sounds good to me," Sully replied.

"We can take a look at the schedule and see what game works for you, Sully. I usually go to one game every month," Johnny said.

"OK, sounds good, Johnny. Let's go to a Sox game."

Johnny called Sully and said, "I got us tickets to the Red Sox Baltimore game in June. Buddy, gotta love it, baby!"

"Nice. Looking forward to going and having a good time with you, Johnny."

"We'll have a blast," Johnny said.

"Sounds great, buddy. We'll have to get together before then," Sully said.

"Absolutely," Johnny replied. "I'm wide open. Just let me know when you can get together."

"Will do, buddy."

"Hey, Sully, I almost finished writing a book about how me and my brother Ray grew up in Lowell, Massachusetts."

"That's awesome, buddy."

"It's not a happy book. A lot of bad things happened to me and Ray growing up."

"Sorry, buddy. It's good you're getting it out there, though. It must be like therapy for you, though, writing it?"

"Not really. I still have nightmares every night from growing up, and they get more severe when I write."

"Have you tried to get help from a trained professional?" Sully asked.

"Yes," Johnny replied. "Nothing works for me; I still get nightmares every fucking night! What are you gonna do—I just deal with it."

"I can't wait till baseball season starts!"

"I hear you, Johnny," Sully said. "A lot more happening for fun stuff in the summer"

"Yeah, I usually head up to my buddy Brian's lake house when I'm not at Fenway Park. He has horseshoe pits!"

Sully said, "Yeah, me and my wife Cheryl are always busy in the summer. We go to cookouts, the beach, and all kinds of fun events."

Johnny replied, "Yeah, lots more fun shit to do in the summer months. In New England, our summer is such a short season you have to pack in the fun when you can.

"Hey, Sully, I finished writing my book."

"That's awesome. Are you going to get it published?" Sully asked.

"I'm not sure," Johnny replied.

"You should," Sully said.

"I have to get ahold of Micky to make sure he's OK with being in my book for a little bit."

"Micky Ward?" Sully asked.

"Yeah," Johnny replied.

Sully said, "Your best bet is to go to one of his charity events."

"Yeah, good idea, Sully. I'll ask him at the next event that he's doing."

Another year went by. Johnny went to a Red Sox game every month the Sox were in town. Sully couldn't go to any of the games because of family obligations.

Chapter 18

The following April Johnny received an invite to go to a benefit for opioid abuse; Micky was going to be one of the keynote speakers. It was a good cause, and it would be good to catch up with Micky, as Johnny has not seen him since Ray passed away. The last time Johnny had seen Micky was backstage at the Golden Gloves at the Lowell Memorial Auditorium. Johnny was hanging out backstage with Micky and Ray. Johnny was laughing and joking with Ray and talking about the boxing matches at the Golden Gloves.

Johnny decided to go to the benefit for opioid abuse with his girlfriend, Audra. They arrived at the benefit around five thirty in the evening. Lots of people were coming up to Micky and asking to take a picture with him and talking with him. Johnny waited till the last person was done talking with Micky, and he went up to say hi. "Hi, Micky, it's Ray Mullen's kid brother."

Micky said, "M&M?"

Johnny replied, "Yeah, M&M's kid brother."

Micky said, "How long has it been?"

Johnny replied, "Twenty-one years." They were referring to how long it had been since M&M passed away. Johnny said, "He's in a better place now, no longer in any pain."

Then Johnny went back to his table where Audra was waiting. Johnny said, "When the crowd dies down by Micky again, I'll introduce you to him."

"OK, sounds good," Audra replied.

About ten minutes went by, and there was no longer a big crowd around Micky. So Johnny brought Audra up to meet him. Micky looked at Audra. "Who is this?"

"Hey Micky, this is my girlfriend, Audra."

Micky replied, "Oh, yeah? What do you do, Audra?"

"I'm a teacher," Audra replied.

"Oh yeah, she keeps you in line, huh, Johnny."

Johnny said, "Oh yeah, she does."

"It was nice to meet you Micky," Audra said.

"Nice to meet you too."

Then Audra and Johnny went back to their table.

Then it was speech time. Leaping Lanny Poffo was up first with a poem. Leaping Lanny was a former WWE wrestling superstar. He recited a poem about Micky Ward that mentioned Rhamalo's West End gym, the gym where Micky trained to eventually become a world champion.

Then it was time for Micky's speech. He definitely had some good one-liners. He said, "I don't know what we are going to do about this drug problem. Maybe we can give it a spinning side kick or an uppercut." Micky's speech ended, and he went to work the room and say hi to the people who had come out for this great cause.

They had an open bar, so Johnny decided to have a few beers. He went up to the bar to get another Bud Light, and Micky was getting a drink at the same time. Johnny and Micky started talking while they were hanging out in front of the bar. Micky had just turned fifty. Johnny asked him, "Did you do anything special for your fiftieth, Micky?"

"No. I took it easy, but I had fun for my fortieth."

Johnny was facing Micky, and Johnny got a tap on the shoulder. Johnny spun around, and the guy said, "Do I know you?"

Johnny replied, "No, but you probably know my brother, Ray. You might know my buddy Micky standing next to me."

The guy said, "Yeah, I know him, but I want to hang out with you." And he hugged Johnny.

Micky laughed and said, "M&M."

Johnny took his drink back to his table, where Audra was talking with a nice gentleman who had introduced himself and kept her company while Johnny was talking with Micky. Audra was feeling tired, so she said, "Are you ready to go home? I'm tired."

"OK. Just let me say goodbye to Micky." Johnny went up to Micky and said, "I have to go, Micky. My girlfriend is tired. It was good to see you again after all this time. Have a good night, Micky."

Johnny started walking away, and Micky put his hand on Johnny's shoulder and gave him a pat goodbye. Johnny left feeling good, as if he had put some of Micky's and his bad feelings of how Ray passed to rest finally.

Chapter 19

The next day Johnny went to the cemetery to say goodbye to Ray and finally put his brother to rest. When Ray died, Johnny never really dealt with those feelings. He just suppressed his feelings and never dealt with them fully.

Johnny got to his brother's headstone and said, "I love you, Ray, and miss you more than you will ever know. I hope you are no longer in any pain.

"Love you, Ray. Goodbye, my brother. I will think of you every day.

"A day has not gone by since you died that I have not thought of you in some way. You are missed and loved by many.

"I hope you have found peace in death that you could not find in life. I have to go, brother. Goodbye."

Johnny got in his car as the sun was setting and drove off, looking back at his brother's grave. He drove out just as the caretaker was getting ready to lock the gate. It was the end of the day and Ray and Johnny's sad journey.

Fade out as the cemetery gate closes behind Johnny's car.

The end